Kittens

Written by Don L. Curry

Illustrated by Cynthia Jabar

Scholastic Inc.

**New York   Toronto   London   Auckland   Sydney
Mexico City   New Delhi   Hong Kong**

ISBN 0-439-13190-1

12 11 10 9   5/0

Printed in China   62

Can you see 1 kitten?

Can you see 2 kittens?

Can you see 3 kittens?

Can you see 4 kittens?

Can you see 5 kittens?

Can you see kittens?

I can see kittens!